Feather from the Firebird

Sacha Abercorn

SUMMER PALACE PRESS

First published in 2003 by

Summer Palace Press
Cladnageeragh, Kilbeg, Kilcar, County Donegal, Ireland

Printed by Nicholson & Bass Ltd.

A catalogue record for this book is available
from the British Library

ISBN   0   9544752   2   4

This book is printed on elemental chlorine-free paper

for my father

Biographical Note

Sacha Abercorn is the founder of the Pushkin Prizes Trust. She received an Honorary Doctorate from the University of Ulster in 2003.

She is a descendant of the Romanovs and of Alexander Pushkin, the great Russian poet.

CONTENTS

Dressing-table

On tiptoe I could see across the glassy landscape of her dressing-table. Just within reach an ink-blue eye-bath full of cold cow's cream waiting for the ritual to begin. She patted the cream all over her face and especially around the scar on her neck. Her neck bandaged for the day ahead in a choker of pearls.

Burial

We stood by those seven small coffins in the centre of the towering Cathedral, as they rested from their long journey. Mother, daughters, granddaughter – sentinels on the last stage of their earthly passage. The choir was assembling and rehearsing. The lights of the big cameras spot-lit the catafalque, bathing it in warm light. No one else was around for that extraordinary moment. Time was put on hold and in the stillness of that second, I heard her say *Have no fear for us, it is we who pray for you. Love is never ending.*

How Much Do You Love Me?

She held us cradled in the big stripey swinging seat, lulled to and fro in a kind of trance, the warmth of her arms smelling like new-mown hay. The links in the chains from which the seat was suspended rasped slightly and she asked us over and over *How much do you love me?*

Forebears

She fell in love with him before the Revolution of 1917. She was the most enchanting woman, the exact counterpart to the irascible man she married. Because of the Pushkin blood in her veins, she and he were exiled from Russia and so my family survived.

Himself

His graceful, reed-like figure touching the clouds, immaculate, debonair, soft-smiling, intelligent, thought-provoking. Atuned to nature and her rhythms, yet logical, even cynical. An unanswered question as to the meaning of it all. Yet he had all the answers. A deep magnet within him drew every beauty to his arms, tender and considerate. Charm like no other. To sit on his lap, as we did every winter evening, and be carried by his gentle timbre into a world of witches and ogres, otters and winged eagles who would rescue us from the clutches of darkness and take us to the light. He made fear a friend.

Sunflower

Such power to charm, to bewitch, with the tilt of the head like a sunflower slowly angling into full sunlight. The amethyst colours of her attire, the sparkle on the lapel, the diadem in her hair. A glass in hand raising the spirit to those she loved – the banishment beneath the table to those she disdained. But I remember her most in the crowd, as they reached out to her – their touchstone.

Cabochon

Blonde and beautiful, beribboned in blue. Flirtatious and capricious, determined and controlling, sentimental and insecure. The House of Hannibal and Romanov coursing in her veins. That sapphire on her finger. Sparkling in her hair, a firefly.

Panda

I was barely five and feeling so thrilled with the most
magnificent panda I had just been given, brought from
America. We were standing under the huge branches of the
old cedar tree in the garden. He thought it would be fun to
take my panda and suspend him from a high branch of the
tree with his belt. Anxiety crept over me when I saw no
signs of panda coming back. So with all the force that I
could muster, and going puce in the face, I demanded that
he give me back my panda. He was amused by the tiny red
shoe being stamped with all its might on the rock-hard
ground. He laughed … my fire fled. Fury and hurt festers in
the dark.

As Above, So Below

That first encounter with her was as if arranged by a
guardian angel. I had just come through a rough passage.
My boat, battered and bashed from the storm of the high
seas, limped into the safe-harbour of her room. Gathering
all the wreckage together, I dropped anchor and slowly, bit
by bit, examined the fragments of it all. Her anchor held the
depths. Her loving energy over time gave me the strength to
mend my sail and once again journey out into the ocean,
but this time aligned to the power in the mainmast, drawn
to magnetic north.

Splints

Night after night, just before going to sleep, the steel callipers were strapped to his little legs. White crepe bandages were wound round and round and round, immobilising his knee joints so that his legs would be perfectly straight. He suffered in silence, the stiff upper lip becoming his prison.

Soap-suds

His frame so secure and sensual, his hands that wrapped us
in rough towels after the soapy bath, full of rainbow bubbles
ballooning overhead, dripping soap in our eyes as we
followed them up and up and up.

Scar Tissue

Tiny needles like sharp pitons piercing scree on a silently
thawing mountainside. He took the pulses in both my wrists
and set to work dissolving scar tissue impacted with time.
Ice warmed by his touch split apart, deep ache dissolving
into crystal clear water.

The Return

A dusky winter's evening was closing in and we had just come back into the warmth of the house. There, curled up in the pink armchair like a small hedgehog, was a figure clad in a thick grey sweater, muddy wellington boots, tousled fair hair smothering her face. She had run all the way from boarding school, crossing roads and fields to get home. A flood of anguish engulfed me, echoing in every cell of my body that sense of desolation – and I would have to return her.

Pushkin

A coal of burning ebony, passionate fire uncontainable,
destined to burn a trace through the strictures of tsardom.

Pushkin was happiest writing from the womb of his bed.

I see him now, sitting by her at the hearth. The night closes
in as she tells him the stories of his land – wolves and
witches take form in the flickering firelight.

He laughs and teases with rapier agility.

Drawn like a moth to the flame of the feminine. The quill
that he held between thumb and forefinger like a feather
from the breast of the firebird.

Too hot a coal to hold for long, he burnt through the very
fabric of his time.

Tuning Fork

He wheels through the air, words swirling like leaves in a gust of wind. Settling into his lofty eyrie, he eases her ruffling feathers as the song sounds its first note.

The Otter

After tea on dark winter evenings he and I would clamber onto his lap. I can still feel the rough scratchy texture of his tweed jacket against my arms and legs and the smell of faded pipe-smoke around him. It felt so safe and secure – the two of us together in the warmth of his arms as we settled down and prepared for our next adventure. Clinging onto the otter's slippery wet coat, we held tight as it carried us on its back downstream. The water cooled and refreshed us from the long walk through the dark forest. We had almost given up finding our way out of the darkness when a tiny white feather floated down and he caught it in both his hands.

The Accident

Four small jet-black ponies hit the big beer barrel with the wheel of their carriage. Their drivers tipped out, ponies hurtling down the grassy hill, the very devil at their heels. The blue rope that I'm sheltering behind becomes taut as a catapult as they career into it. Falling to the ground and like a huge snake rushing at me, it grabs my ankle and flings me into the air …

The Bite

We were eighteen months apart, as close as two peas in a pod. That summer day they had taken us to visit friends of theirs. He and I were standing at the top of stone steps, stunned by the fact that I had just sunk my teeth into his best friend's chest and drawn blood.

The Open Cage

Confined to comforting conformity, frighteningly secure, unaware that the iron door above lay open, she sniffed the air, wet whiskers shivering in the chill of night. A shooting star streaked overhead and as it caught her glance she saw the opening. Stretching to her full length, her black sleek form eased its way up and out. Eyes like golden embers lit the ground beneath her as she tentatively placed her velvet padded paws on the stony soil. She kept night-watch until dawn began to break, loath to leave and live.

Chameleon

That chameleon-like quality. When travelling far he seemed at home in any land, to be alive to every sense as if he belonged there. Colour, texture, taste were heightened so that the memory of every voyage with him has never dimmed.

Geese

She had her sentries posted at the door the day he and I went to visit her. Three fierce geese, their necks arched, beaks pointing at us, guarded the pathway we had to navigate. She seemed so far away, so out of reach that we both stood there paralysed with fear. Then, as if a sound could break the spell that had entrapped us, we heard the jingle-jangle of her gold charm bracelet. In a flash we were in her arms.

His Birth

Signals of his imminent arrival that night came like gentle morse code, the tapping out became insistently stronger, building into rhythmical waves that swept all of me into its grip.

Onto your surfboard, one step at a time, this is the only one you have to deal with.

The waves built up to a crescendo of unrelenting force, a giant tourniquet, pressure perfectly designed to push, propel, project him into life. Breathing deeply as she taught me, fear fled with the ebb and flow of the iron tension in the muscles. Those muscles that had elasticated to extraordinary lengths over the months to cradle so securely his shaping form. Such a momentous release for both of us as he slipped out, a warm weight in my arms, ocean-blue eyes, clearly focussed, carrying knowledge from the deep.

The Branding Iron

The sword she carries touches him with the power of her presence. Gentle beauty acknowledging the sacrifice he has made, branded at birth to serve. A flowing mantle of midnight blue enfolds him as she sets the seal with chain and ribbons, honour harnessed in symbolic armour. A warrior of the spirit in her defence.

His Hands

He was a master of his art. Each piece of antique beauty that he touched came back to life in every limb and breathed anew. A skin of sheen, a suppleness of form, a glow for all to see. But down below, in the deep dark chasms, those eddies swirled and dragged him off to the land of the gods from whence he had come.

The White Tiger

A thundering rumble in the valley, I recoiled in instant
recognition of what I had to face. In a bound he was beside
me, shattering my plate-glass defences.

Snake Belt

Wrapped round his waist like the Ouroborus, a small brown snake felt at home. He had found her as he walked in the grass and he carried her back to show us. We stood by the privet hedge outside the house awe-struck by the mystery and power that embraced him.

The White Stone

Surfacing from the deep dark, aching and bemused, half-light my friend, soft sounds, stillness in the spine as it stretches out along the rock that radiates a healing lightness from below, softening the shock.

Gazelle

She stood motionless for a moment by the front door, heavy bags at her feet, gathered up for the long journey home. The beauty of the hind on the edge of the forest sniffing the air, alert for any untoward signal. Poised for flight.

The Kiln

Earth and water mix into a malleable clay that turns on her wheel, raw life in her hands, waiting for the kiln door to close, for the firing to be complete. Only then will the phoenix rise from the ashes.

Wedding Day

The days of loving detail that had gone into the preparations for your special day were crowned by the morning itself. I found you standing alone by the window, tears in your eyes like drops of rain magically turning into sunshine as a rainbow filled the sky and held us in its arms.

Breakthrough

Tall, damp grasses, fresh and green. A wide-open summer-
time meadow. A river flowing, North-South in the distance.
Sparkle of light on water. In the foreground a large tree. The
trunk is dark and the branches spread so high and wide that
I can't see them all. I walk round the tree. A small doorway
in the rough bark at the eastern side draws me to it. I enter
through the opening into a circular room. There, a window
faces west, and I can see the meadow and the river. In the
centre stands a circular piece of wood, yew I think, like a big
table-top, rough and old, many circles giving its age. As if
from overhead, a film of light, a shower of silver pours
straight down through the middle of the table. As I watch,
this laser light pierces the wood and it breaks open in front
of me. Light pouring down through the floor into the deep
dark below. Watching like a silent observer, the shaft of light
now strengthens and thickens as a green, sap-like thread
snakes its way up the column of light past me at eye-level
and on, up and up, into the branching of the great tree, now
becoming illumined from within, dancing with a spiralling
energy.

The Bantam

We were all on the overnight sleeper, all of us, including a family of four bantams. They had been surreptitiously smuggled on board in their travelling box and hidden underneath the bunk bed in her cabin. But horror struck as Jack, the young cockerel, awoke to greet the dawn, his clarion call more penetrating than any alarm clock. She leapt out of bed, seized the unfortunate fowl and wrung his neck.

Arriving home, we grimly gathered round the bantam box, opened the lid and to our utter astonishment, out popped Jack, head angle-poised. After that he was on the warpath. He never forgave her.

Breakfast

The end of a long dark night in below zero temperatures, well wrapped in my sleeping bag. I had slept and been dreaming for probably eleven hours, with the odd wakeful adjustment having to be made to the bones of my body aligned to the earth. The early sun woke me with a cold glow through the ceiling of my yellow tent. I lay for a while gazing at the light until a greater warmth broke through. My spine tingling as if the rock beneath was radiating a life-force. I sat up slowly in the cold air to dress. It had to be done in a special order. The most vital thing of all was to keep the woollen hat on my head. Opening the zip to a freshening draught of morning air was exhilarating. Stepping out into the vitality, the energy swirling around was almost tangible. First to release the warm waters of the bladder, welcome nutrients to the earth herself. The washing of face and hands and teeth in freezing water from the dromedary bag hanging on the tree by my tent and then breakfast. There can be no more delicious, saliva-awakening sensation than mixing a little powdered milk with ice-cold water from the creek and pouring it into the pine-green bowl of sweetened granola.

A Solo Passage in the Chiricahuas

Pot-bound, cramped roots, coiled into a container like seething snakes, bursting with urgent energy to search for their source. Journeying back to the desert where it all began, sun baking earth and rock, penetrating deep into the hardened skeleton of her body. Light seeping through all forms and structures, connecting up the web. Wisdom uncoiling, serpentining from the depths where she sleeps. Revitalising every sense. The phallus flowers.

The First Root

Like shimmering jewels in a casket buried in dark earth, he showed me the icons. Healing holy figures of former times, now rooted underground, harbingers of Sophia, the rising sap of our time. He guards the portal and gathers from all around, those who hold a key.

Echoes

Echoes of her earth-trembling voice reverberate through me now. Why such silence? What is held back? A leaden mood of quiet despair descends and the line of least resistance is to sink. Deeper and deeper out of reach. The fear of being unloved or unlovable, if truly known by those around; of no value in the absence of a voice. A lifetime's recognition for that false façade. So what to do? Perhaps just be.

Partridges

They had been hatched in the warmth of the linen cupboard, the eggs turned and dampened every day until the time came for the tiny beak inside to tap with all its might and break the painted shell in half. She fed the four on chopped-up egg and minute flies until those tiny balls of speckled fluff grew wings. Every night they followed her up the stairs to sleep, nestled into her eiderdown, taking shifts to stay awake, guarding her like winged sentries. At moments during the day she would make a curious high-pitched call *weeny-wat* and they would scurry to her as if in response to the dinner bell.

And so in time we became the weeny-wats – all five of us – and that same call would bring us to the table.

Butterfly Siesta

A whirring of perpetual motion day and night, ideas
cascade, focussed on for a moment, flown from, and then
returned to at some later date. A ceaseless vibration of
colour in flight. A pause, then the wings fold for a siesta.
One moment's freedom from the never-ending tick of time.

Silent Tears

Strapped into her high-chair patiently waiting, a hubbub of voices surround her as we gather round the table. But why those silent tears running down her rosy cheeks like raindrops on a windowpane?

The Cub

He left her side so very young, so unprepared for the far-off jungle, to join a pack of growing males, all searching for the paradigm. In his nostrils he sniffed the rusting iron of her cage, his soles cracked against the rough concrete of the floor. An echo of her desolation touched his soul, but the inexorable thrust for light and life in fine new growth drew him on to a twilight path to stalk the threshold stealthily.

The Christening

We gathered inside the ancient rock-face, a small band of
Christians, Orthodox and Muslims, all travellers in
Armenia. Rough-hewn steps led up and into an open sacred
place where a family gathered for the Baptism of their child.
The priest leading the ceremony totally immersed the child
in a pool of water. Then out of the blue he led us all in
English, saying *Our Father*, dissolving in an instant the
borders that lay between us.

Touching Aphrodite

Lying in a warm sea-water pool, buoyant, weightless, down in the belly of the earth, in a bath of bubbling foam, jets pummelling every part of the body, froth playing on the surface of the twilight world from whence she comes. A timeless moment in the realm of Aphrodite attended by her silken-haired hand maidens. The heartbeat is restored in tune with that deeper pulse.

On Board Ship

We had paid our dues to Neptune as we entered his
Equatorial kingdom. Great brown bears had smothered us
with foam. The barber with an outsize cut-throat blade
seized us and we were unceremoniously dunked and almost
drowned in the pool. This strange ritual is performed on
anyone crossing the line for the first time. However it was
not just Neptune that we would encounter on this voyage.
Sailing on through an ocean of petrol blue serenity, the sun
setting, silhouetting against the horizon a small cocos-
palmed island, musicians on deck playing glorious show
tunes when, as if choreographed from the deep, a school of
dancing dolphins encircled the boat, surfacing in perfect
rhythm. Aphrodite's chorus line rehearsing.

Hesychia

We are conditioned from the moment we take our first breath, to fill every second of our waking life with action – with the doing of something. We are measured and valued by the results of these actions as if that is all that counts. But true embodiment can only be found in the fusion of touch in luminous darkness, the spark of stillness.

Agatha's Tree

She used to visit us nearly every school holiday, and especially in the summer. She loved the huge fir tree in the garden that was also the garden shed. Underneath its great drooping furry limbs was an entrance into a deep hollow in its side. Forks and rakes and spades were stored, all kept perfectly dry. On certain days I got a sense that Agatha was flying by. I would tell the children that this might be the moment to call her in. Busily, fir cones and petals were laid out ceremoniously on the stone slab at the door of the old tree. After a short time they would run back to see and I would hear euphoric shrieks of *Aggie's been and she's left us Smarties this time.*

The Call of the Muses

To be faithful to one muse is a challenge. To be called by three and respond to their demands, is something else. He acknowledged the call of the artist, the musician and the composer. The muses bestow their favours on him, but the sacrifice he pays is daunting.

Uniform

He touched our life with fun and humour, standing over the
gas stove, making fudge surrounded by his grandchildren. A
military manoeuvre of timing and precision. He was
murdered because of that for which he stood.

Beauty

I heard she had been killed in a car crash on her way to post a letter. She was like a summer's day in childhood.

The Parrot

Huge spiney wings beat the air with blue and scarlet. Sharp claws grabbed the shoulder of his jacket as it sunk the curve of its black beak into his ear. Horror-struck, I hid behind him, turned to stone.

High Expectations

A young, full-blooded filly of perfect conformation, bred to stay the course. Who would have known how that schooling was to have been tested in the cruellest challenge of all.

Copyright

Have you ever gazed at a tiny, four-petalled purple flower
and wondered what could be the intelligence that informs
such touching beauty? From what source can such
wholeness stem? From the smallest seed in darkness to the
fullest bloom of unfurled perfection. Might that not be the
thumb-print of the maker – the blueprint in us all?

Horse Whisperer

He gathers up the lengthy lungeing rein in both his hands,
the spirited filly gently held, responding to the tension of his
firm control. A skilful mastery that requires of him the self-
same reining of the colt within.

23rd August

I write the date at the top of the page and like a magnet drawing myriad memories, fragment-like through the ether, they coalesce into a mirror-ball of shattered beauty.

Curlew

The cry of the curlew echoes across the valley, soft mist rising from the River Don. His ashes scattered by the one who followed him too soon. To the father and the son.